CONTENTS

Chapter 1
The Curies

In 1897, Marie Curie and her husband Pierre lived in Paris, France. Marie had moved to Paris from Poland in 1891 to study physics and math at the Sorbonne. At the time, the Sorbonne was the only university in Europe that allowed women to attend. Pierre ran the laboratory at the Municipal School of Industrial Physics and Chemistry.

Marie, it's time to go home. Irène needs her parents, and we need our sleep.

I have just one more note to make.

7

Marie looked for substances similar to uranium and tested them with the electrometer.

Just as I expected!

Thorium and a few of these other substances act just as uranium does. They give off their own energy.

Next, Marie decided to try some substances that contained only small amounts of uranium.

Now let's try the pitchblende.

9

CHAPTER 2

THE DISCOVERY

Pitchblende was considered mine waste after the uranium was removed. Mine owners were happy to give it to the Curies for their experiments. Only a very small amount of uranium remained in the pitchblende.

The Curies knew that elements were rare finds in the world of science. So Pierre put his own experiments on hold and began to help Marie.

Let's give this element a name.

I'll call it polonium, after my homeland.

The Curies continued their work with pitchblende. Soon they had discovered another new element.

Pierre! This new element has even more radiation energy than the polonium.

We'll call this element radium.

And we'll call its energy radioactivity.

CHAPTER 3
RADIUM AND RADIATION THERAPY

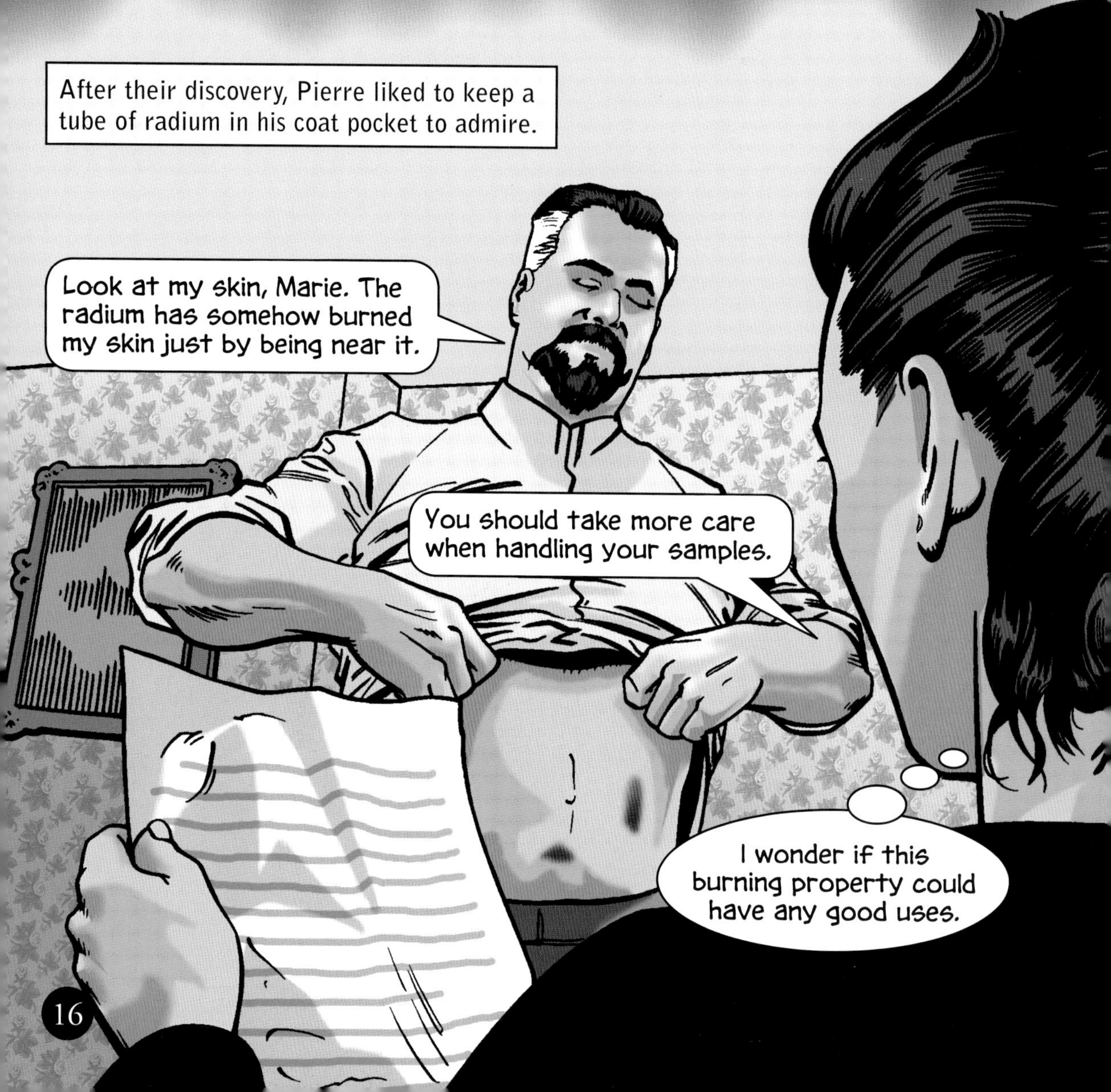

The Curies didn't worry about damage from radiation. Instead, they told the world of its possible good uses.

You see, by burning unhealthy cells, radiation therapy could kill off harmful cancer cells.

Amazing! This radiation therapy could rid the world of cancer!

Soon, radium was in common use. People thought radium had healing properties. Department stores even sold lotions and shampoos made with radium.

In 1903, the Curies and Henri Becquerel were awarded the Nobel Prize in Physics for their work with radioactivity. At the time, Pierre and Marie were too sick to attend the ceremony.

These types of prizes create too much attention from the press.

I agree.

KNOCK KNOCK

One would like to dig into the ground somewhere to find a little peace.

In 1904, Marie gave birth to a second daughter, Eve. Marie continued to work in the lab and at home. But Pierre was becoming even more ill.

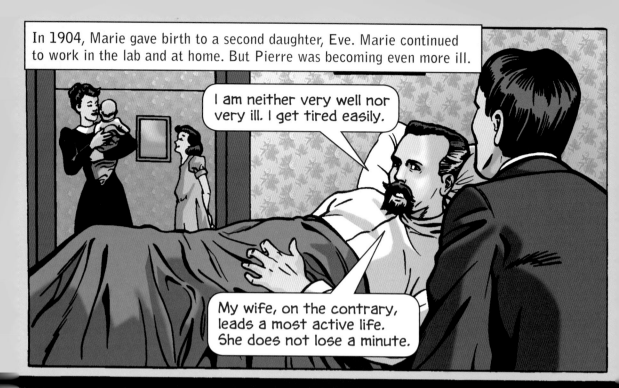

I am neither very well nor very ill. I get tired easily.

My wife, on the contrary, leads a most active life. She does not lose a minute.

Only two years later, Pierre was struck by a horse-drawn wagon and killed. He was 47 years old.

Good-bye, Pierre. Your coffin is closed and I can see you no more.

Despite her grief, Marie continued her work. She began to teach at the Sorbonne.

In 1911, Marie's hard work paid off again. She won a second Nobel Prize. This time, the prize was in chemistry, for her discovery of polonium and radium.

I accept this prize in honour of my late husband, Pierre.

Three years later, Marie opened the Radium Institute in Paris. She had worked hard to raise money for a better laboratory with more assistants and lab workers.

Half of the Institute is used to study the medical uses of radium.

The other half is the lab where we will be studying radiation.

Marie drove some of the vehicles to the battle sites herself. Irène, who was 17 years old at the time, often helped her mother.

Well, Irène, I am about to drive us straight into battle.

You are brave to do it, Mother.

Well, there was no one else.

The shrapnel showed up very well on the X-ray.

I'd like to assist you in removing it, doctor.

Of course. You know, Madame Curie, countless soldiers will survive thanks to this X-ray equipment.

Irène Curie and her husband Frédéric Joliot continued to study where Marie left off.

In 1935, Irène and Frédéric earned the Nobel Prize in Chemistry for their discovery of artificial radioactivity.

Your mother would have been so proud!

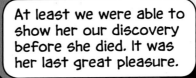

At least we were able to show her our discovery before she died. It was her last great pleasure.

MORE ABOUT

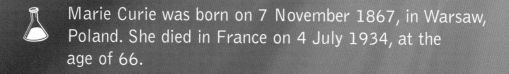

MARIE ✱ CURIE
AND
RADIOACTIVITY

Marie Curie was born on 7 November 1867, in Warsaw, Poland. She died in France on 4 July 1934, at the age of 66.

Marie invented the term *radioactivity* to describe the energy given off by polonium and radium.

Marie took notes in her laboratory notebooks while doing research on radium. As a result, the radiation that harmed her body also got into her notebooks. Even today, Marie's notebooks are too radioactive to handle safely.

After the Curies discovered radium, many companies wanted to use it in their products. Marie and Pierre could have made money by patenting their process for collecting radium. Instead, they believed radium belonged to everyone. They felt other scientists should be allowed to find ways for radium to benefit the world.

Marie is the only person ever awarded two Nobel Science Prizes in different subjects. She won the Nobel Prize in Physics in 1903. Her 1911 Nobel Prize was in chemistry.

Marie's mobile X-ray vehicles were nicknamed *petites Curies,* or "little Curies". By the end of World War I (1914–1918), Marie's fleet of 20 *petites Curies* had helped more than 1 million soldiers.

 Marie and Pierre studied ways radioactivity could be used in medicine to help people. But the discovery of radioactivity also had a negative side. It led to the creation of the atomic bombs the United States dropped on Japan near the end of World War II (1939–1945).

 In 1995, Marie's and Pierre's remains were moved from their original burial site in Sceaux, France. They were reburied in a place of honour under the dome of the Panthéon in Paris.

GLOSSARY

element basic substance in chemistry that cannot be split into simpler substances

persecute cause to suffer

physics the study of matter and energy, including light, heat, electricity, and motion

radiation tiny particles sent out from radioactive material

radioactivity a process in which atoms break apart and create a lot of energy

uranium a silver-white radioactive metal that is the main source of nuclear energy

INTERNET SITES

http://www.mariecurie.org.uk/aboutus/MarieCuriethescientist/

This page provides a brief profile of Marie Curie, the inspiration behind the founding of the Marie Curie Cancer Care charity.

http://www.mariecurie.co.uk/

This website lists key dates in Marie Curie's life and provides quotes from and about her.

MORE BOOKS TO READ

Curie and the Science of Radioactivity, Ian Graham (Barron's Educational Series, 2006)

Marie Curie (Great Lives series), Philip Steele (QED Publishing, 2007)

Marie Curie, Kathleen Krull (Viking, 2007)

Marie Curie, Vicki Cobb (Dorling Kindersley, 2008)

Marie Curie: Mother of Modern Physics, Janice Borzendowski (Sterling, 2009)

The Search for Radium: Marie Curie's Story, C. Birmingham (Mathew Price Ltd, 2006)

FIND OUT MORE

Marie Curie's office and personal chemistry laboratory have been preserved at the Curie Museum in the Institute Curie.
26 rue d'Ulm
75248 Paris cedex 05
France
Telephone +33 (0)1 56 24 55 00
http://www.curie.fr/fondation/musee/index.cfm/lang/_gb.htm

Visit the tomb where Marie Curie's ashes are buried and where she was the first woman to be so honoured.
Place du Panthéon
75005 Paris
France
http://www.pantheonparis.com/

INDEX